A Dorset Country Calendar

A Dorset Country Calendar

Andy Case

Roving
Press

Published by Roving Press Ltd
4 Southover Cottages, Frampton, Dorset, DT2 9NQ, UK
Tel: +44 (0)1300 321531
www.rovingpress.co.uk

First published 2012 by Roving Press Ltd

ISBN: 978-1-906651-12-1

British Library Cataloguing in Publication Data
A catalogue record for this book is available from the British Library

Artwork and photographs by Andy Case
Cover design by Roving Press

Set in 11.5/13 pt Palatino Linotype by Beamreach (www.beamreachuk.co.uk)
Printed and bound by Henry Ling, Dorchester.

In memory of Jane Ling,
who convinced me that I could write.
For my wife Maureen ('the Missus'),
and for my favourite niece Jenny,
this book is lovingly dedicated.

Contents

Foreword

It is possible to go for a stroll across the fields so engrossed in conversation, if in company, or absorbed by thoughts when alone, that on returning home you are not aware of having seen much. The fresh air will have done you good but the wonders of nature may have escaped you. This is often what differentiates those of us who live in the countryside from 'the countryman'. A countryman is attuned to things around him, he doesn't miss a trick – a weasel darting across the path 50 yards ahead, the alarm call of a jay in a nearby wood, a pigeon flight path denoting their choice of a certain field to feed in, little messenger clouds warning of changes in the weather. He sees his surroundings as a matter of course and the author of this delightful book is one such person. A stroll in the fields becomes a rich chapter of the happenings in the lives of those who share the land with us.

Not only has Andy written of all these goings-on with informed delight and charm, but also his talents have encompassed creating the lovely illustrations, worthy of any *Observer* book. The reader will find several references to the knowledge imparted by 'the old men'. I have knowledge that the author is not younger than me and has, therefore, moved into the realms of the 'old men' he refers to, i.e. those noted for sagacity and quiet knowledge (my words not his!).

When this is shared with us in the many gems among these pages, it gives us all pleasure – especially the little personal touches.

Colin Seaford
Long-standing friend,
Bush Farm Bison, West Knoyle

Preface

We came to Long Ash Farm in the parish of Milton Abbas just after the Second World War. In those days it was a mixed farm of 200 acres with cows, sheep, pigs and corn, along with poultry, a cart-horse called Prince and turkeys for Christmas. I left school at age 16 and came straight home to work on the farm. When I took over the running of it, I just grew cereals and kept beef cattle.

Forty-five years on, since we supposedly retired, my wife and I have drastically reduced our acreage, and we now specialise in the Oxford Sandy and Black breed of pig. With both sows and breeding gilts* we run 30 females and three adult boars. We bring on several young boars and gilts every year, some to keep and the rest to sell. We hope to sell all the progeny as 8-week-old weaners, usually one-third for breeding and two-thirds for buyers to finish to pork or bacon.

This book is based on the monthly columns I write for our village publication *The Bulletin*. It came about after several readers said to me they thought my articles would make a good book. These monthly offerings, collected over a 4-year period, are inspired by my observations of the wildlife, weather, local matters and farming around the parish of Milton Abbas, on our farm and those of our neighbours. My aim is to interest readers in the intimacy of the countryside and farming, so that they might appreciate a way of life that they may not have been brought up with.

I have been published before. Some years ago I was asked by a publisher to expand a booklet I had written which he had picked up from our stand at the Royal Agricultural Show. The subsequent how-to-do-it book *Starting With Pigs* went on to be a phenomenal success. On the strength of this, a much larger publisher sought me out to write the introductory chapters and pig descriptions to a sumptuous coffee-table book called *Beautiful Pigs*, which is distributed worldwide in four languages.

My wife Maureen and I enjoy all the facets of our farming life, with our deep love of the countryside and our animals and, more particularly, our pigs. We are privileged to live and work in the beautiful Dorset countryside, out in the fresh air. It has always been a great help and comfort to be able to call on the wisdom and common-sense imparted to me as a boy by the old men who used to work for father and on our neighbours' farms. Their knowledge was freely given and willingly received. I thank them all.

Andy Case

Acknowledgements

I thank my neighbours and dear friends David and Noel Hosford for their encouragement and insistence that I should publish this book; also Peter Chafer, Editor of *The Bulletin*, for publishing my 'Case Notes', which in effect brought this book about. Finally I should like to thank Laura Henderson for her enormous help editing with her computer, for typing my scribbling, and for being a big part of the effort in bringing this book to fruition.

*Note: words that might be unfamiliar to readers are asterisked in the text and explained in the Glossary at the back of the book.

The Old Men

Uncle Fred Sharpe

He came from humble beginnings and a big family. His love of Shorthorn cows enabled him to rise from farm boy to head stockman and eventually to marry the farmer's daughter. He had an instinctive touch with livestock and indeed all animals. He loved a bit of fun which always included the passing on of his wisdom.

Grandfather

Grandfather, mother's father, married a farmer's daughter from Hinton St Mary. His father had a joinery shop at Parkstone from which grandfather ran R.J. Bishop, master builders. He was a wealthy man and set up a trust for my two brothers and I to be well educated. He bought Long Ash Farm in 1949 for mother and father.

Old Joad

We had to call him Mr Joad. He was the farm foreman when we were boys. A quiet man, we learnt our skills and knowledge of farm work from his example and friendship. He made wooden whistles from green elder twigs for me and my brothers and showed us how to use hand tools and our muscles effectively, which has stayed with me all my life.

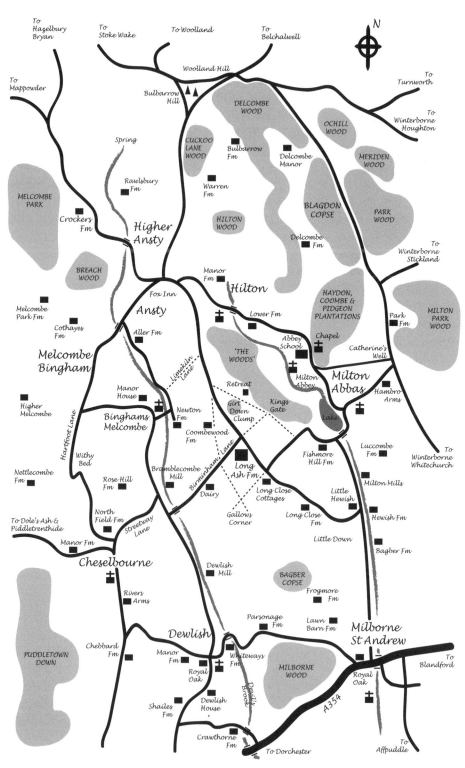

JANUARY

Isn't it lovely to see snowdrops and aconites in flower again? They never fail to appear to lift our spirits in the winter gloom; the two together make a real splash. Before Christmas we had primroses flowering up in the woods, not that that is unusual, but none the less welcome so early. There are hazel catkins on bare branches and swollen buds on the sycamore trees proving nature is already starting her cycle again.

The recent cold snap has one advantage; it brings a wealth of birds to the bird table and feeders. We find so many song birds cannot resist black sunflower seeds, particularly finches and the five types of tits that come. Our spotted woodpecker always turns up at the beginning of winter and, at long last, the beautiful long-tailed tits have arrived. The disadvantage of a spell of freezing weather is that the drinking water for the pigs must be carried to them. Pigs don't mind the cold weather; in fact as long as they have a warm bed, adequate food and occasional sex they're as happy as Larry!

Here at Long Ash and on our neighbours' land there is no shortage of skylarks. The popular belief that farmers are to blame for the death of these birds and others, including lapwings (peewits in Dorset) and house sparrows, seems incorrect. While the Missus and I were walking the dogs, we put up 26 skylarks. We have seen ravens again. These large black birds are recognised by their being

Skylarks

Ravens

1

always in twos, and by their deep croaking as they soar above or sit atop a tall ash tree.

~

I think the Gulf Stream must have changed course to flow up the Channel, it's been such a mild winter. 'All to do with global warming,' they tell me. There are quite tender plants still flowering in our garden that should not be. We still have argyranthemums, lobelias and brachycome blooming away when they should have died back long ago. Up in the woods there are not only a few primroses flowering but whole drifts of them, not just a posy but a really big bunch there for the picking. We met some friends from Leicestershire. They told us that they still had caterpillars eating their broccoli in the middle of January.

It came as a bit of a shock then to have the wind change round to the north and blow nearly a gale last Sunday. Monday afternoon saw me all wrapped up against the cold feeding the pigs, when a young lady, Robert Bagwell's daughter (the Bagwells, late of Delcombe), and her artist husband came striding up, heads down against the wind. They had come she said to ask if he might do some paintings of your pigs. They showed a genuine interest in them and the Oxford Sandy and Blacks in particular. So I up-ended my feed bucket and sat down to discuss the merits of the pig.

We had our backs to the wind, facing the winter sun sinking like a gold ball in a yellow sky. Slowly the cirrus clouds changed to be edged with pink. As we chatted they dulled to grey, then back to a gold horizon before disappearing; but the best was yet to come – that peculiar green light you get sometimes just before dusk, a light that is ethereal, of mystical grace, of the first sight of the evening star. Even cold winter evenings are blessed with beauty.

~

January last year was filled with flowers. Plants and shrubs in gardens and woods bloomed exceptionally early, with frog spawn in the pond and bumble bees on the wing. Not so this year. We are back to normal. Snowdrops and aconites started flowering in the middle of the month and that's it, but there are many green shoots of promise.

It is nice to have the goldfinches in the garden, but they are so quarrelsome, seeing off their larger cousins, the greenfinch and chaffinch. I suppose being so gaudy, with their red, white and black head, they can get away with it. We are delighted to have a nuthatch on the peanut feeders. I know many people who always have them, but it is the first time they have ever visited us. We haven't had long-tailed tits so far, although they are in the lane at the top

Greenfinches

of the Six Acres. We have pied wagtails with us all year but never on the bird table before, but when we had a sprinkling of snow they

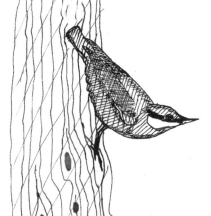

Nuthatch

came, obviously very hungry to be so bold.

Every morning first thing, when I step outside the back door, the song thrush up in the great ash tree beside our cottage sings his clear, happy notes, which lifts my heart as he repeats each refrain three times over, and later when I'm mucking out the pigs I am serenaded by a robin atop the pigsty's roof.

Yesterday I saw a weasel running along the top of the backyard wall, and now the peewits are back on the winter corn. Years ago plover's eggs were eaten as a delicacy, but you just try to find a peewit's nest on the ground nowadays. The old

men had the trick. With two cart ropes* joined together and from the middle of the field, they would peg one end, stretch it out, then walk round in a big circle. When a sitting peewit was disturbed it would fly up. All they had to do then was walk the rope to find the eggs.

In the New Year I drove over Bulbarrow Hill to go beating* in a hoar frost* that reached over the top of the tallest trees. The sun was low in the sky, lighting them to fantastic effect, and everything sparkled.

Thrush

Peewits

To get through the winter the hedgehog relies on the fat he put on in the autumn. He sleeps on until the sun is warm enough to lure him from his bed. On fine days field voles and squirrels raid their food stores. The mole is always active during the winter. He throws up his molehills night and day. The old men say he works 3 hours on and 3 hours off. He needs to catch his weight in worms every day to keep himself alive. They say the molehills you see in straight lines are the work of the male. Those that are scattered around are the workings of the female; or is it the other way about, I can't remember? I do know that often the straight line of molehills leads to where the mole drinks, where he has to come above ground.

Those downpours we had earlier washed away soil to reveal stones and occasionally fossils. At Long Ash we find fossils dating from 195 to 135 million years ago. Out walking the dogs, with a rivulet running down the lane, the Missus picked one up. My books told me it was a Neithea, a sort of cockle shell from the Lower Cretaceous period, about 135 million years old. We also find Micrasters, a heart-shaped fossil with a starfish impression, and Cornulus, what we call 'Shepherd's crowns'.

One afternoon the wind dropped, the sun shone in a cloudless sky, the frost thawed from the ground and I slithered in the mud. I struggled to maintain my footing with a bucket of pignuts and three old sows determined to knock me over. Out of the corner of my eye I saw a red fox trotting, loose-limbed, lazy, lit by orange sunshine, the light that glows before sunset. He made the length of the brambled hedge and then I saw the object of his desire – a cock pheasant in his blazing bronze plumage, with dark green head and white collar. He saw the red fox coming and looked up, pecked once more, then turned and slowly disappeared into the thick hedge. The fox, he just sat down in the slanting sunshine and the quiet of the afternoon.

FEBRUARY

My neighbour's ploughman is almost unique because he ploughs with a conventional plough. It has a single set of right-hand mouldboards*, as opposed to a universally used reversible one. A reversible plough has two sets of mouldboards, turn-furrows we call them, left-hand and right-hand. This enables him to work from one side of the field to the other by simply ploughing down the field with a straight furrow, turning on the headland, reversing the plough and coming back again. With a conventional plough it is necessary to plough in 'lands'. The ploughman strikes out a ridge and works round it, up one side and down the other. He then 'gathers' two lands together to fill in and repeat this until the area is finished. Lastly the perimeter is ploughed, the headlands and sidelands.

Before tractors, the single-furrow horse plough cut only a 10-inch furrow, so the ploughman had to mark his field out with very narrow lands. He started with a three-quarter land of 17 yards, and the rest at 22 yards or one chain wide. There is a metric aspect of the chain measurement; it has 100 links – one link though measures 7.92 inches! I still own a chain with its long links, handles either end and brass tags to mark the quarters.

Further back in time, when oxen pulled the farmer's plough, his team worked for 220 yards or 10 chains before they stopped and returned down the field. He carried a goad to encourage the oxen to pull well up into their yokes. The goad was a 5.5-yard-long rod, pole or perch. The ploughman took his 220-yard furrows (our furlong or long furrow) and

by laying the goad across his ploughed land four times, he measured a chain. One chain wide and 10 chains long is an acre. George Voss of Parsonage Farm, Dewlish, owned a team of oxen and ploughed with them during the 1920s. The last time to my knowledge an oxen team ploughed was at Manor Farm, Dewlish, in the early '30s.

I never got bored when ploughing. The tractor cab was ideal for watching wildlife – foxes, rabbits and badgers by night, pheasants, wheeling rooks and many songbirds by day; seagulls, of course, following behind to pick the worms; and the view from Long Ash Hill and the ever-changing sky.

~

This must surely be an early spring, what with everything sprouting and plants bursting into flower. The grass is growing like the clappers. An early turn-out for the cattle this year means so much less work from the endless round of carting food to housed beasts and having to clean up behind them.

Just as a matter of interest, I looked back in my diaries to 1984. Twenty years ago it was also a leap year and, like this one, it was an early spring. On the 5th of February I noted that the snowdrops were nearly over. On the 14th I wrote that the primroses were flowering in Three Acre and on the 25th celandines were in flower. Contrary to common weather lore, February is one of the driest months of the year and, also contrary to popular belief, spring growth starts more or less at the same time every year. It is the cold winds of March or April that set the early growth right back again.

The rooks have started nest building. If they build them at the top of the tree, the old men say 'it'll be a good summer' and if they build them low then 'it will be bad'. The rook is by far the commonest species of the crow family. Its bare, scurfy, white face distinguishes it, when adult, from the crow. The sexes are alike, but the young have feathered faces. The rook is a great digger and for this reason he is tolerated by the farmer because he eats leather-jackets*. However, he also eats grain, particularly when it is in the milky-ripe stage. It attracts hundreds of rooks to flop down on the crop and lay it flat, much to the anger of the farmer. Nobody shoots rooks now. I'm not surprised; rook pie is pretty disgusting!

Rook

~

'When the wind is in the east, baint no good to man nor beast,' as the old men say. It's true an east wind is a cold quarter, but it's always a dry one – except when it brings snow. Yesterday I heard that distinctive 'whooping' sound and looked up to see a pair of

Canada geese

swans overhead beating their powerful wings into a headwind from the east. A few minutes later a pair of herons flew over, one behind the other, the back one making its creaking croak. In the early '50s our old postman was Harry Lovell. He was always prophesying snow because he had seen a goose fly over. It's a common occurrence nowadays, as there are so many Canada geese everywhere. In those times the geese he saw were probably pink-footed or Brent and one did see them aloft when it was very cold,

There are signs that spring is not too far away. When we walked the dogs earlier this month, we saw celandines, violets, red campion, mini cow parsley and dandelions in flower. The pheasant cocks are sparring and cock blackbirds are having dust-ups. In the woods the jays are making their fearful racket. It must hurt their throats to make such a dreadful noise. I often think when our donkey Amy starts up, it must cause her terrible effort to create her wheezy honking. Today a mob of magpies was kicking up and rowing

Jay

over a mate. When we were children we used to kiss our palms in quick succession to mimic the magpie's call. We could bring them in quite close because the bird is very curious.

These winds have really dried the soil, so that we are able to

roll the winter corn fields (and push the stones down) and sow the spring corn. Young lambs can stand this weather whereas cold driving rain kills many of them. It is so dry and there is so much grass about that my neighbour has put his cows out for an early bite.

Early last month I went out to feed the pigs, up the garden steps, through the back gate to the quad-bike, when a tawny owl flew into my legs. It glided just off the ground to land on the bonnet of the Land Rover. I did not investigate further as I had a lot of hungry mouths to feed. When my wife came back from feeding the dry sows* and poultry, Sky (our German Shepherd) was barking at the shrubs behind the Land Rover. The Missus went to see and picked up the tawny owl. It was excessively thin and so weak she had no need of gloves. She put it in a bird cage with a very low perch and some raw meat. It was not able to feed itself at first, but with a little help it ate a good meal. In the afternoon all the meat she had left had gone. It appeared a bit stronger. The next morning it was listless and not able to eat and by lunch time it was dead. Like all animals and humans, it rallied before it died. It seems to be a sure sign of impending death.

One afternoon when I arrived down the field on the quad-bike to feed the sows, a buzzard was perched on a large sod of earth thrown up by the pig as she rooted. He stood alert ready to snatch a worm, ploughed up by the sow's snout. The buzzard took no notice of me as I filled the bucket and the old sow lumbered over for her feed.

We have a lot of pheasants which come to feast on pig nuts* at feeding time. They come in four colours; most noticeable are the melanistic* ones. Then there are the Old English Blacknecks, the Ringnecked and the Mongolian, which has a break in his white ring at the collar stud. Some Ringnecks have blue-grey rumps and are called 'grey-backs', though I think they should be called 'blue backs'. The hens vary in colour too, from the very dark melanistic to the 'washed out' ones we used to call Bohemian.

MARCH

Yellow is for spring; primroses, daffodils, celandines, forsythia, hazel catkins, pussy willow, brimstone butterflies and yellow-bottomed bumble bees. We've passed the vernal equinox so now it's officially spring, with the rooks busy and a robin sat on eggs in our garden shed since the 13th of the month. We have frog spawn and tiny tadpoles, but not many.

It's a busy time on the land, ploughing and cultivating the soil ready for sowing, and the chain-harrowing and rolling of grassland. I have been chain-harrowing our grass grounds to tear out the dead mat of grass in the bottom of the sward*. Last year we did not buy any cattle to keep our grass down. We decided to keep about 4 acres from being grazed or mowed. This is an ancient and natural method of providing feed for stock during winter. This 'stood up hay' is called foggage.

It's a real treat to be out in the sunshine during this lovely dry spell. We and the animals alike crave the sun at this time of the year. We all feel better with sun on our backs. It is from sunshine that we get our vitamin D.

As I feed the pigs in the afternoon the rabbits scurry up the old badger bank, their cotton tails bobbing. They scamper between the thorn bushes on cropped grass enamelled with daisies and violets. with vivid wild garlic leaves limply waiting for their stars to rise. Such quiet, except for a breath of north wind padding in my ear, the rhythmic munching as the pigs eat their nuts and a pheasant, which flops over the hedge with a swish of gold-brown feathers.

I certainly put the weather into reverse by writing of an early spring last month. The cold weather brought the long-tailed tits back to the bird table. I think they are my favourite tit of all, with their round, fluffy, pink bodies and long jerking tails. There is a pair here and with luck they will nest in the garden. We might then see their pretty little fledglings.

Long-tailed tit

During the return to cold we had a vixen come right up and pinch the pig nuts in amongst the sows and the old boar. It is odd how hungry wild animals adapt behaviour quite contrary to their normal ways. After breakfast, when I went out as usual to give the pigs their fodder beet* by throwing whole roots over the fence, the fox, more audacious than ever, picked up a beet and ate it. Not its normal diet I would have thought. She then came every day to carry off a beet. One morning the vixen came back for a second one, having buried the first. Now I have seen chicken corpses buried when Charlie* has visited and practically wiped out the cockerels we were fattening for eating. She showed so little fear of

Fodder beet

human presence at this time. Perhaps Mrs Charlie is now becoming a vegetarian? Not permanently I think.

The only wild animal we have that shows no fear of man is the shrew. It gives off a musky odour which wards off most predators, but owls kill many. Pick it up, put it in your palm and it won't run away. After the shooting season closes pheasants are much more conspicuous, none more so than in hard weather. Usually 16 hens come to snaffle the pig nuts when I throw them to feed our sow Jubilee and her ten piglets.

Pheasant

We do not give animals enough credit for their intelligence. I once watched our old Arab mare push a thistle over with her front hoof so that she could more easily eat the grass it protected.

Now that March is here, shrubs, perennials and bulbs are at their flowering best. It's a time for hope and expectation. The earliest tree to have its leaves is always the elder and of course the honeysuckle. Sycamore buds are green, the chestnuts sticky and the hawthorn, in sheltered hedges, is showing leaf, along with some blackthorn bushes which are just coming into flower.

Celandines are out everywhere, in the woods and lanes, with their luminous yellow heads and carefree manner in the number of petals they display, anything from six to nine! The delicate wood anemone, the nodding wind flower that shines amid the verdant green, decorates the woodland floor. The crows are patching up their nests and the wood pigeons are pairing. Brimstone butterflies dance up and down the sunny bank and a host of honey bees descended on the heather bed in our garden, on the 17th of March, the day the temperature went above 60°F – the first time we have seen bees in the garden in such numbers since Varroa disease hit the honey bee population with such devastating effect.

Something else that has come back is the pair of wild mallard ducks we had last year. They came to our empty duck pond and brought off nine beautiful ducklings. This year we have three call ducks* on the water; despite this the wild mallard drop in several times a day and I feel sure they will stay. Last year the parents flew off when the ducklings were nearly full grown. Sadly they all left too.

～

We found the first primroses out on the 1st of March and the first frog spawn on the 8th. Despite the cold winds and weather, 'the spendthrift crocus, bursting through the mould, naked and shivering with his cup of gold', adorns the garden, with a mass of hellebores nodding in the wind.

One really cold morning when the ice was thick, I went round the end of the pigsties to feed up, when a rat shot by me chased by a rabbit which veered off at the last minute. I could not believe my eyes. I thought rabbits were the hunted and not the hunters, or were they just belting along the same path, who knows?

It was at this time that we had a treecreeper in the garden. We had never seen one here before and I have never had the chance to study one. The little bird, only 5 inches long, is brown above and white below. It is the only British land bird with a curved beak. Being secretive it is heard rather than seen. It has a very high-pitched, unmistakable call which is always delivered from the top of a tree. The treecreeper runs up, sometimes spiralling up, trunks, always starting at the bottom, stopping frequently to probe crevices of the bark. It will hang upside down on the branches.

Treecreeper

While feeding the pigs I noticed a raven land, with swift and silent flight, close to a sow for some pig nuts. He must have been hungry, for pig nuts would not have been his normal diet. They do eat practically anything but mostly carrion. What surprised me was that almost immediately he was mobbed by jackdaws, which flew at him and got him airborne again.

APRIL

The robins in our shed have fledged and flown, while the blackbird in the chicken house stuffs worms down her chicks. Jackdaws persist in ramming sticks down our chimney and nature's hand has whitewashed the blackthorn bushes. This year, like most, we've had a 'blackthorn winter' with five really hard frosts and then straight into summer! I hope enough of the later blossom survives to produce a harvest for sloe gin. My father used to say the 'blackthorn winter' has nothing to do with cold weather, it's just that white blossom looks like snow on bare branches.

Robin   Blackbird

While walking the dogs on a recent warm day, we were overcome by the sweet scent of a line of blackthorns in full bloom. The intense heat lifted the perfume and a hot wind wafted it straight up our nostrils. We have never smelt blossom like it. But bluebells beat all for scent and indescribable colour. They are probably at their best now; sadly they won't last long if it doesn't rain.

Continuing our walk, we scuffed the white dust up along a chalk cattle race, bounded on one side by a big hedge and a border of wilting nettles on the other; we saw a host of butterflies – tortoiseshells, peacocks, brimstones; there were also a good number of orange tips (the male) and the smaller, all-white female. The real delight was to see a holly blue, just the one. This sky-blue beauty is another of our early butterflies which overwinters as an adult.

Everybody must want rain soon! Our garden, on solid chalk, has many wilting plants. Those harsh frosts didn't help and the drying wind finished the job off. While clearing away an old poultry pen at the bottom of the garden, we discovered a hedge sparrow's beautiful nest in the Lonicera with four lovely blue eggs. Hooray! I've just seen my first swallow. But I am still waiting to hear the cuckoo.

~

I have seen orange tips, three common blue butterflies and three swallows, all on 24 April. I haven't seen those lazy, flying, black insects with dangling furry legs that often bump into you. They are called St Mark's flies because they emerge on St Mark's Day, 24 April. I have never heard of any folklore about them, but in times past, when mowing grass for hay and singing to keep boredom at bay, they would fly straight into your mouth. No radios or cabs then!

Swallows

One of the nicest drives must be to go from here across the hills to Beaminster. The first hump is over Streetway Lane into Cheselbourne, round the school and up Drake's Lane, with its banks of celandine and stitchwort. Driving over the top again, down into Kingcombe, up to Thorncombe and on to Dole's Ash. Hardy wrote a poem about Dole's Ash (Flintcomb-Ash).

WE FIELD-WOMEN

How it rained
When we worked at Flintcomb-Ash,
And could not stand upon the hill
Trimming swedes for the slicing-mill.
The wet washed through us – plash, plash, plash:
How it rained!

How it snowed
When we crossed from Flintcomb-Ash
To the Great Barn for drawing reed,
Since we could nowise chop a swede.
Flakes in each doorway and casement-sash:
How it snowed!

How it shone
When we went from Flintcomb-Ash
To start at dairywork once more
In the laughing meads, with cows three-score,
And pails, and songs, and love too rash:
How it shone!

(Thomas Hardy)

As you drop down the hill to Piddletrenthide, Chris Suter has his Flintcomb Nursery on the left. Coming out of Piddletrenthide we climb another hill with its wonderful views and lovely countryside, to cross over the old Sherborne road to Cerne Abbas. Then across the top of St Catherine's Hill to quaint Cerne with its ancient history. Up the hill opposite the Cerne Giant to Crown Point, dropping through banks starred with primroses to the water splash of Sydling Water. Up and over the A37 skirting Cattistock, through the hamlet of Sandhills and over the railway line to Lower Wraxall, where time

has stood still. Then on to Higher Wraxall to Wraxall Manor, surely one of the most exquisite houses ever built. Up again to belt along the main road past the wireless station, to turn at last for Beaminster, to drop into the bowl where the charming little town nestles, where my favourite niece lives and where I get my quad-bike fixed.

A lady tackled me the other day. She was adamant celandines always have eight petals. I insisted the number varied. 'How do you spot the odd ones?' she asked. It's observation, training one's eye. My wife homes in on our four-leaf clovers all the time. All the books on our shelves have four-leaf clovers pressed between their pages. I found a celandine with ten petals. Wood anemone flowers are pretty perverse too. They have six, seven or eight. Sometimes you can find pink ones. There's a group of them over the old Abbey wall, up the drove from Kingsgate.

Stoat

A young man spoke to me outside the village post office. 'Stoats and weasels – which is which?' he asked. Old men used to tell us boys that 'weasels are weasily recognised, but stoats are stoatily different'. The weasel is about half the size of the stoat's 14 inches. He has a thin snakelike body. Both have reddish fur with white underparts. The stoat has a black tip to its tail, the weasel does not. In the far north the stoat's coat turns white in winter, except for its black-tipped tail. It is its white fur and black tip that is the ermine which is used to trim the ceremonial robes of the Lords.

Some people have all the luck. My farming neighbour saw a red kite the other side of Dewlish at Warren Hill. There is no mistaking this bird, it's the only hawk with a forked tail, and yes, they are down here in Dorset now. Last summer he found a kingfisher in his kitchen. He caught it just to confirm its extraordinary blue and that its beak is almost half its body size, making it such a good fisherman.

This spring he has a buzzard's nest on his farm and rooks have built a new rookery in his copse,

Red kites

abandoning the old one they have used for generations at Newton Farm. What, I wonder, makes rooks pack up and move? It happened when Dutch elm disease killed all our elms, but the Newton trees are still alive.

—

Kingfisher

Has summer come in April, or did a drought year start in March? The drought of 1976 started at the end of March and finished the middle of September. We all completed the harvest by the end of July that year, and the crops were, in many cases, less than a foot high. The whole countryside went brown as the blazing sun beat down relentlessly.

In the old days farmers welcomed a dry March, the better to sow the spring seeds. A dry time was needed to cultivate the fields to bring the couch grass roots up on top, which were horse-raked into rows and pitched into 'hipes' (heaps), then burnt. An old man would spend all day tending his couch fires with 'only thin smoke without flame', as Hardy wrote. In a wet time, father would get Henry Hole, the agricultural contractor from Clenston, to bring his single-furrow 'Prairie Buster' plough with its enormous mouldboard. The theory was to plough the couch down so deep, about 18 inches, so it wouldn't grow again. His man, old Eddie Pavey, would arrive on his boom-boom tractor, a single-cylinder diesel Field Marshall. Eddie amused us boys because from the bottoms of his trousers and around his neck we could see his pyjamas. As the sun rose higher, Eddie would put another 'cwoat on to kep the het out'.

The old men say that the wood anemone heralds the coming of the swallow, and that the fairies sleep in the closed flower at night. I saw my first swallow on the 10th of April. The male comes first to the exact spot it was hatched, the females arrive 14 days later and about a mile from their birthplace – seems a bit fickle; though, thinking about it, if the females came back to theirs, there could be some that might mate with their brothers.

Everything is flowering and greening early in the garden, as if they need to do it quickly to make seed so that they can survive the drought. Only our walnut tree is till stubbornly dormant. On Butler's Hill there's a crop of winter barley coming into ear 4 weeks early; and on the 21st of April we saw a fledgling song thrush in our lime trees by the road. Thrushes are doing well at Long Ash.

MAY

The hawthorn is the May tree or 'bread and cheese' tree as it is known in Dorset – May tree because it flowers in the month of May, bread and cheese tree because children, myself included, used to eat the young leaves. They were very pleasant, in the days when country children never had enough to eat. It is not a big tree but a shrub, not awe-inspiring like the stately oak. It is not long lived and yet the leaves were carved in wood and stone in our ancient churches and cathedrals for perpetuity. The hawthorn was always held as sacred, and still is by some old countrymen.

It was the lover's tree in poetry. A single tree growing by itself, we always thought of it as the fairies' tree and as such it was never cut down or disturbed. May boughs were used as the protectors on May Day. They were placed around the bottom of the maypole and the Queen of the May was dressed in green and crowned with May blossom. Great grandfather and his pals placed hawthorn boughs under the bedroom windows of their intended before they proposed to them.

May blossom

My father, as with most country folk, would never allow May blossom to be brought indoors because it was deemed unlucky; and yet some think the blossom is supernaturally powerful against evil and witches. It was thought to be magical, good as a protective hedge, for walking sticks and for the power of good.

The old men always quoted this couplet: 'Under the thorn our Saviour was born'. The May blossom is exquisite with a strong almond scent and is a magnificent sight in bloom. To sniff the blossom has a strangely calming effect on all and by doing so, it is believed, nature gives us a tiny piece of herself – a little part of the whole picture of the countryside in which we farm, labour or live, while we are here for our allotted span and then return, as all must, to the soil.

For me May is the best month. The whole countryside is alive and green. All nature is striving to reproduce itself for another year. The creatures are in a frenzy of activity; the sun climbs ever higher in the sky and the warm rain drips from the eves of the thatch and sparkles after a shower, 'For bright is the sunshine after rain'.

~

I don't think I have ever seen the May tree look so voluptuous or so beautiful. If it was not such a common hedgerow tree you could kid your townie friends that the lovely tree you planted in your garden was a 'such and such' from Moldovia and cost you a fortune! The blossom, when looked at closely, is exquisite. The delicate, milk-white flowers have a lovely almond scent and they taste nutty too.

Last week we took pigs to the Devon County Show. It was a pity that there were not more Oxford Sandy and Blacks there to give us more competition, but we were still pleased to come home with the Breed Champion and Reserve Champion as well. Showing one's stock, in my opinion, is the best yardstick to measure your pigs against other people's. I love to learn, to chat and share a jar or two with pig-men and old friends. It is a delight to see so many high-class, well-scrubbed pigs in the ring. It's interesting to try to pick the same pigs as the be-suited and bowler-hatted judge does, and in

the same order. It makes a good break from the routine to put your stock before the public; it is a perfect way to advertise them.

I like to peruse the cattle lines to see cattle of perfection and stroll amongst the sheep pens; to stand and watch the cheap-jacks (the stall-sellers) as they shout out their practised spiel to sell their 'wonderful vegetable cutters'. Agricultural shows are hard work and very tiring but most enjoyable. I love the month of May with new leaves on the trees and everything flowering; the lanes laced with frothy cow parsley and the elderflower just coming out. The old men say that the summer starts when the elder is out, and it finishes when its fruits are ripe.

~

This cold May has been no good for the butterflies. I have seen very few. Bumble bees fly at low temperatures so they have been buzzing around the garden. When we were children and went to the Milton Abbas village school, we would catch the big bumble bees, the drones, in our cupped hands and chase the girls around the playground. The male bees do not sting but they frightened the girls with their buzzing.

Milton Abbas

The old men hold great store in observing the behaviour of the bees to foretell the weather. Like all animals they are sensitive to the winds and weather pressures.

'A swarm of bees in May is worth a load of hay'
'A swarm of bees in June is not worth a silver spoon'
'A swarm of bees in July is not worth a butterfly'

(early swarms are best for the colony or hive of bees;
a late swarm does not bode well for plenty of honey)

This May has not fulfilled her promise and yet, one day when the heavy rains of the afternoon passed, the wind died, the sun came through to light up all the raindrops and the tarmac road began to steam. Then the blackbirds sang in the still of the scented evening. And when the last blackbird stops singing, so the old men say, Brock the badger comes out to play.

I always think that May is the pinnacle of spring, when nature has her floral dress on, with her best green waistcoat and highly polished shoes. The month was dry until the third week when it all went wrong and was then cold and wet. Our pigs didn't like it and stayed in their arcs. The Oxford Sandy and Black is prolific, hardy and docile; big pigs, pale ginger with black spots and white feet. The breed has a history that stretches back 250 years. They were the

cottagers' pig and probably had Old Berkshire, Tamworth and Old Gloucester Spot in their make-up.

We have had trouble with a hedgehog eating the chickens' eggs. The Missus put the nest box up on the chicken house roof. That stopped him and the hens continued to lay in it. We forgave the hedgehog because he eats the slugs and snails in the garden. I was asked, 'How did you know it was a hedgehog that ate the hens' eggs?' It is very simple; a hedgehog eats a hole in the side of an egg, whereas a jackdaw or magpie pecks away to split the egg into two. If the egg disappears then a crow has carried it off or a rat has rolled it away. If all the eggs are smashed and their contents eaten, then a badger is to blame. The other evening, on going out to check a sow in the farrowing* shed, I was stood under a full moon having a pee when I heard some snuffling. 'That's hedgehogs,' I said to myself. I crept up to some long grass and saw two of them mating. 'How do hedgehogs mate?' I hear you ask. The answer is of course very carefully!

JUNE

As I drove over the top of Bulbarrow Hill, heat shimmered off the hot road and huge cauliflower clouds climbed up and across the sky. If the weather stays like this for tomorrow, I thought, it will be perfect for me to go gliding. I dropped down the hill from Cuckoo Lane to Ansty Cross, where three old men with walking sticks sat on the memorial bench in the shade.

When I got home the Missus came to the garden wicket* to tell me that a lady had just stopped to say we had some piglets on the road. All piglets are Houdini's but when they get to a certain age, it is the devil's own job to keep them in. We went down the road and around the corner, yet they were nowhere to be seen; but when we looked in their paddock they were back in with their mother as good as gold.

This meant I had to do some fencing. I hate the job, but it was a lovely day, with goldfinches on the thistles and daddy long legs on the cocksfoot* tussocks. That done I went for a cup of tea. All the flower scents in the garden were suppressed by such a sticky afternoon. I sought the shade in the backyard to drink my tea and watch the odd busy bee. It does not seem long ago that our lime trees almost roared with the sound of the wing-beats of thousands of bees as they worked on the lime tree flowers, sadly not now though, due to Varroa disease in the bees.

Goldfinch

After tea we rode the horses out on a favourite ride over Coombe Hill. As you drop down to Newton, the down is covered in wild flowers – scabious, harebell, trefoil, knapweed, red bartsia, thyme, late purple orchid, oxeye daisy and stemless thistle – and many butterflies. There is a beautiful restful view as you look across to Binghams Melcombe, which always lifts my heart, the little church of St Andrew, crouched among its graveyard yews and bounded by its neat hedge, confirms the permanency of the scene.

Much later I thought I would go to the badger bank in the Six Acres behind our cottage to wait and see old Brock emerge from his sett. Badger watching is a bit like fishing, it can be the most uncomfortable, fruitless waste of time you can indulge in, what with getting cramp and gnat bites. But after sunset when the world breathes slower a different life begins. When the badger comes out to sniff the air, then the wait is all worthwhile.

~

'A leak in June brings harvest soon'

(showers in June help to ripen the harvest and fill the grain)

'You wait till Wimbledon,' the old man said. He was quite right of course, Wimbledon started and so did the rain, the wind and the cold. I'd been complaining that it was too warm and dry. The peas were drying up and the pods not filled, and flowers in the garden only lasted a day or two and then shot to seed. We could have supper in the backyard though, and afterwards sit on the swing-seat until all the stars appeared.

The heat accentuates the floral scents in the evening. The smell of the dog rose and the honeysuckle in the hedgerow is sublime. Further away and wafted by a gentle breeze, my neighbour's field beans in flower were heavenly. I remember that when I was a small boy, I would lie on my back in the bean field with a girl I was sweet on called Paula, almost comatosed by a million bean flowers' erotic scents. We would stare up into the blue and count the passing fluffy clouds and the towering skylarks. Ah, those halcyon days; so many hopes and no homework.

Skylark

Spotted woodpecker

We have some excitement in the garden; the pair of spotted woodpeckers have brought their young to the peanut feeder. They are truly striking birds with red bottoms and powerful claws. The brood certainly eats mountains of peanuts in a day. We have a lot of butterflies around but, unlike last year, very few varieties. There is almost a plague of meadow browns. I have seen one marbled white, which is always a delight.

～

I have never been to the Derby, I haven't got a top hat, but Derby Week always registers for me as the week that partridge chicks hatch. I can remember seeing some, still with eggshells stuck to their rears, fleeing down our sun-scorched, dusty lane. They can run and feed themselves as soon as they are hatched, just like ducklings which plop into the water and swim as soon as they emerge. It is said the reason for the partridge's decline is the lack of the right insects for the chicks to feed on.

Partridge

We find the only place to walk the dogs when it is so hot is in the woods. The green shade is cool and calming. The birds fall silent; they have been up since 4 o'clock for the dawn chorus. Hungry youngsters need feeding several times an hour and the days are so long. We were amused to watch our spotted woodpeckers teaching their young to feed themselves from the peanut feeder.

Under the yew tree is the most shade, although it was said that if you fall asleep under a yew, you might not wake up. Yew trees were planted to mark ancient boundaries. Just over the brow of Monmoth Down there is a line of them. The Hambros, the family who purchased the Milton Abbey estate in 1852, planted it up as a shoot, to make the pheasants fly higher. On the ground they planted box, snowberry and guelder rose for cover and feed. They are still there; some of the box are as big as trees. Yew trees look dark in a wood, 'blacker than night'. They have an aura of mystic depth and yet are fabled to keep away evil. In Dorset and Wiltshire too, the yew beside the farmhouse, cottage or church was planted to keep demons away and give comfort and were originally for protection from the coldest winds. There is a large yew outside Long Ash Farmhouse. They are, of course, poisonous, bark, leaves and berries. The coral-coloured seed coating is sticky and sweet, which we sucked when we were children, then spat the seed out! The yew grows best on chalk and gives shelter to a host of birds.

~

The ground is so hard and dry with a scorching wind that has made the flowers flop and quickly go to seed. It is the sort of wind that gets under the cat's tail, which turns him into a kitten. He dashes around the garden with his tail crooked and zooms straight up the cherry tree trunk. He hangs below the first branch with a silly look and has to reverse back down, whereupon he rushes off to play with the pebbles on the path.

This weather is perfect for hay-making. Not that much is made these days, but when baled with the sun on it, you can open a bale in winter and smell the sunshine. Hay-making was hard work 40 years ago, but I look back on it with fond memories. The tea-times we all had in the field when mother brought the plum jam, crusty

sandwiches and homemade lemonade, and one of her sponges filled with raspberry jam and cream. It was such a social affair, as it was laced with the wit of the old men, with their bottles of cold tea, stoppered with plugs of grease-proof paper. We had such fun as we boys dropped hay seeds into their mugs and had to dash off to avoid the back of their big hands and their good-humoured scoldings.

The honeysuckle, rose and lavender scents have been subsumed by these sticky afternoons. When the rooks adorn the top of the old ash tree in the pig paddock, being irritated by the heat, they shout at one another before they float down to earth to steal the pig nuts which I have just fed to the dry sows. But we have had some memorable scented evenings. As the air cools we sit outside eating supper and linger until the last blackbird sings himself to sleep, when all is hushed and the dew creeps up the couch grass stalks.

JULY

'Fast runs the ant as the mercury rises'

(ants move faster as the temperature rises)

This extreme hot weather slows us all down. I like summer, but this degree of heat I find hard to work in. Our pigs struggle in this weather too as they do not sweat. When a pig pants it is excessively hot, but their panting is not effective in getting rid of heat. They are not like a dog in this respect. Generally it is not sunburn in pigs that we worry about, it is heat stress. Coloured outdoor pigs do not suffer sunburn, while white pigs, like the Middlewhite can get burnt, particularly the piglets, and so care should be taken with these.

The solution is to provide shade, preferably of a tree, but man-made will do. The provision of a wallow, which the pigs can get into that cools them down, is a great help. In our soil, which has a clay content, we need only play a hose on the ground and in no time the pig will dig its own wallow.

Heat stress is much more acute when a sow is near to or actually farrowing. It is essential to bring her into a cool sty and, perhaps, fix up a fan. If she is still hot, put cold, wet towels on her as she lays there. Vinegar sponged on behind her ears will help to dissipate the heat. Heat stress can be fatal to pigs.

A wallow is good for pigs and for swallows for building their nests from the mud in a drought. The pied wagtail (or 'polywashdish' as it is called in Dorset dialect) loves splashing and bathing in puddles.

Pied wagtail

It bobs its tail and stalks about on the edge of the wallow and flies up to catch the mosquitoes. It is a fact that the pig paddocks are never without a pair of polywashdishes. They seem to have an affinity with the pigs.

This very dry weather is not good for the soft and cane fruit in the garden. The Japanese wineberry, on the other hand, seems to fruit well, rain or shine. I think it must be because the fruits are encased in a calyx* until they are ready to pick, which stops the birds having them. They have a truly superb taste and I cannot understand why they are not more popular.

When I let the dogs out last thing the other night, it was a perfect time after such a scorching day. It was cool then and moonless with stars so close you could reach up and grasp one in your hand. I could even count all seven stars of the Seven Sisters constellation. It is humbling to think that the star-light I could see left them hundreds of years ago, when Queen Elizabeth I was on the throne.

~

The Missus sat bolt upright in bed. 'Why are those broodies* cackling?' I didn't reply and pretended to be asleep. 'Something's wrong, we'll have to get up,' she said.

So it was that I found myself outside at half past three in the morning. It was quite light and we could see a fox sitting in front of the broody pens. They're like cupboards, up off the ground with wire mesh fronts. The fox ran off and the broodies settled down and so did I, back in bed.

The next morning, or the same morning but later, when the Missus went down to feed the broodies and chicks, she found five of them with their heads bitten off – three chicks from one pen, two from another. What possessed them to stick their heads through the mesh, one after the other, and wait while the fox bit them off in turn I've no idea. Can foxes mesmerise chickens as stoats do rabbits? I've long suspected it.

In the garden the mangetout have got their second wind and we are munching away through mountains of them. We've had buckets of broad beans and cart-loads of courgettes. They grow overnight and if you turn your back they've grown into marrows. The Missus has found a very good way of using the surplus. What she can't give away she turns into soup. She renders down a saucepan-full with some stock and garlic and then freezes it for winter use. It is really good with a strong flavour.

It's time again to pick the first runner beans and it's also raspberry time. We've had two good pickings from the wild canes up in the woods. There are rather more yellow ones than last year. It's a funny thing, you never see yellow raspberries advertised in the garden catalogues, but whatever the colour there's nothing like 'food for free'.

—

It only takes a few really hot days for my farming neighbours to quickly make some hay before the corn harvest starts and for all the butterflies to come out. Marble whites, ringlets, gatekeepers and meadow browns we saw as we rode across Coombe Hill.

I have a soft spot for pigeons ('woodies'), even when they peck at our newly planted broccoli. They amuse me as they waddle around the foot of the bird table to pick up fallen crumbs, they are much more adept in the air. We were sat around our table in the backyard to have supper in the 'dog days'* of summer. The tub of lavender at my elbow wafted its scent across our meal, when a woodpigeon landed on an elder bough up the hedge a few paces away. He didn't look at us but seemed content with his own company. We ate cold meat, then broke bread, cut cheese and refilled our glasses and still he sat. Perhaps he was keeping out of the way of the Missus, who nagged him to get supper for the squabs*. Pigeons regurgitate a liquid, 'pigeon's milk', for their young. Perhaps he'd had a hot busy day and wanted some time on his own, in the evening sun, on his bough. Two more pigeons arrived on top of the cupressus, obviously lovers in 'playful rout' as they frantically flapped their wings about. My pigeon didn't stir. The 'Red Arrows' zoomed by, a formation of starlings. They climbed, banked, peeled off and reformed. They must do their aerobatic flying for the sheer fun of it. They're mimics

and comedians with their inane chattering, and the youngsters could be another species, they look so different from their parents, until they get their spots.

The lovers left. Our lone pigeon sat on in the sun. Perhaps he was old and tired. As we cleared and clattered plates and cutlery and sat back down with glass in hand, he was still there. The honeysuckle that flops over the wall of the yard filled our noses. We drank in its scent and our beer as a little frog hopped over the flagstones. My 'woodie' was still there, rocking slightly from side to side in the setting sun, bathed in gold and glory. The phone rang and I got up to answer it, but when I came back he had gone.

—

Come the evening, after the Missus had tipped a bucket of water over a plant that was expiring, the hedgehogs appeared to see if the slugs had woken up. When I go near them they quickly sit down, but on waiting I'm surprised how quickly they move. Hedgehogs seem so squat yet they rise up on spindly legs and run like hell.

Harvest has started and it is zipping along in this baking sunshine. The grain is coming off the combine at under 12% moisture, this being 2% lower than the legal limit accepted by the grain traders.

Enormous machines that cut 30 ft at a pass with air-conditioned cabs clear 80 acres or more in a day. The straw is baled in half-ton blocks immediately and hauled away, all by big tractors and machinery; nothing is touched by hand.

Time was when it took so much longer. The corn was cut with a binder and as it went round and round the ever-decreasing crop held the many rabbits more and more contained until they were jumping over the binder's cutter bar and across the canvases*. Men and children came from the village with running dogs and sticks to capture a rabbit or two for the pot. It was terrific fun as the rabbits bolted.

The binder cut corn just before it was ripe; so the sheaves were 'hiled'* in stooks*, with the knots of each string facing outwards. This meant that when the sheaves were put together the butt ends had a slope to them. Heaven help us if we didn't get it right,

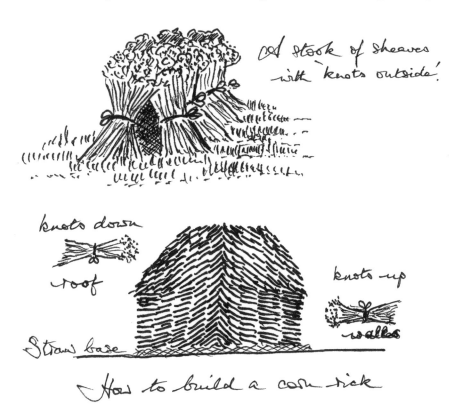

A stook of sheaves with 'knots outside'.

knots down

roof

knots up

walls

Straw base

How to build a corn rick

otherwise the old man would cuss. The stooks were left to ripen and
dry until we had heard the church bells twice. Each sheaf then had
to be pitched onto a wagon and taken to the rick. The wagons were
unloaded by hand to the foot of the elevator which carried them up
to the rick. The boy would pass them 'knots up' to the old man who
built the rick – a skilled job. When the roof was started it was 'knots
down' to give a natural slope as the old man brought each course in
a little, until there was not enough room for the two of them; then
the boy would stand in a 'pitch-hole'* and pass them up with a pick.
When the rick was finished, the old man would 'dress' all round by
whacking it with a shovel to square it up.

The fields were slowly cleared; then women and girls would
glean* the stiff stubbles that scratched their legs, to pick up the
dropped ears of corn and carry them home in baskets to feed the
chickens. Harvest was a time when everyone was involved, when
the church was filled with village folk who were truly thankful for
a harvest safely gathered in.

AUGUST

Farmers have had wonderful times this year. Rain came just right to bulk up the grass, so that huge crops of silage* were cut and ensiled. Then the sun shone long enough for everyone to make heaps of hay. We had a heat-wave for harvest and they romped through their crops without a hitch, so by Gillingham and Shaftesbury Show day we met many farmer friends who were having a well-earned day out with a good harvest behind them.

The elderberries are turning black and when they're ripe old men used to say that the summer was at its end. It has been a wonderful year for butterflies. We have an old plum tree that has diseased fruit on it, which attracts dozens of red admirals. I believe it's no good blaming farmers for the lack of butterflies, as every time we have a really hot summer, and I admit we don't have a great number, we have a bumper crop of butterflies. I have seen painted ladies and clouded yellows; they fly over from the Continent.

Elderberries

Blackberries are getting ripe, and so are the cooking apples.

Nature designed things so well to have them both ripen at the same time. Blackberry and apple pie is surely a gift from heaven. There was a magnificent orange full moon as it rose up from the horizon on the 12th of August. In times past the harvest moon was always noted as a milestone in the farming year.

—

It's not the first time summer has come to such an abrupt end and it won't be the last. Perhaps we'll have a sublime September or golden October. This weather has prolonged the harvest. My corn-growing colleague reports that until the rains the yields were pretty good, but as the wet goes on, the quality and the yields drop; the grain 'grows out' in the ear, i.e. it begins to sprout, or falls out on the ground. It will be a costly harvest now when the grain is wet as it has to be dried and it costs roughly £1.60 per 1% of moisture content to dry it. Grain is sold at 14% so if the harvested grain comes in at nearly 30% moisture, then the profit has gone.

Farmers to the north of us on the clay soil are getting increasingly worried. They cannot nip out with the combine when the sun shines and do a bit, because the ground is so wet the combine gets stuck. There is a second worry in that farmers will not be able to sow the

Wheat   Barley   Oats

next crop. There is little chance that the clay soils will dry out much this end of the year. The later they sow in the year the lower the yield. By sowing early you maximise your yield.

With corn farming margins so tight anything one can do to increase it for nothing is of paramount importance; hence the rush to get a quick turnaround from harvesting the old and sowing the new.

⌒

Yesterday I was excited by an odd occurrence when we were coming home from shopping in town. There is a spar copse* on the right, down the Dewlish side of Warren Hill. At the start of it there are some dead young elm trees – or 'elems' in Dorset-speak. These stark trees have no bark and not a stitch of leaf. The elm is a tree that throws up lots of runners which survive until their trunks grow big enough for the elm bug to get underneath the bark to feed, procreate and then kill off its host. This caused the demise of all our stately elms which succumbed to Dutch elm disease in the '70s.

The odd thing we saw was a 'flight' of swallows that had alighted in the dead branches. Most of the birds flew up as we passed. At first we thought they were a 'chattering' of starlings, but there is no mistaking a swallow. At this time of year swallows gather on the electric wires, but I have never seen one perch in a tree.

Mugwort is a grey-leaved, strong-smelling, medical and magical little herb. It used to be purified in the smoke of the

Swallows

bonfires on St John's Eve (23rd of June) and hung over doorways and in cowsheds to keep the powers of evil away. It grows around the edges of cornfields and is superb in flavouring field mushrooms when fried in a pan. It shows up now after most of the harvesting is done.

It is when rain comes after a prolonged dry time that there is a growth spurt of grass, when cattle eat too much protein. Grass and clover can cause a build-up of gas in their rumens*, which happens mostly in spring-time. They blow up and, if not treated quickly, they die. It always seems to happen on windy days. The old men used to say that cows lick the wind up into their mouths as they tear the grass with their tongues, but I don't think this is right. I

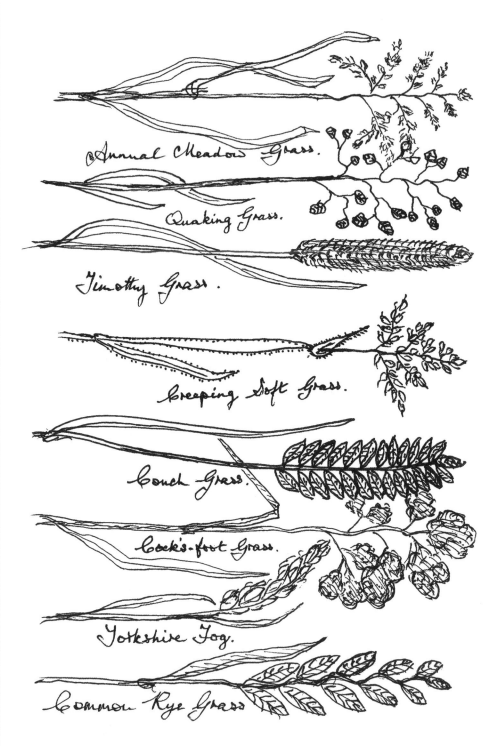

Annual Meadow Grass.

Quaking Grass.

Timothy Grass.

Creeping Soft Grass.

Couch Grass.

Cock's-foot Grass.

Yorkshire Fog.

Common Rye Grass

can remember years ago we had some Ayrshire heifers* at Girt Down Clump at the top of our farm that were bloated. Father got a carving knife and plunged it into their sides to let the gas out. They all survived except one.

~

The Missus has picked a lot of blackberries which she mixes with the Japanese wineberries we have in the garden. These make a good dessert for supper with home-grown vegetables and home-produced pork. There is nothing like eating your own, something you have picked only minutes before. The hawthorns are emblazoned with berries, or 'haws' I should say. If it were the dog rose then they would be 'hips'. When we were children, we would split them open and then slip them down the girls' dresses as they skipped in the playground. They itch like hell.

One tea-time the Missus told me that she had watched a wood mouse bite and eventually tear off a portion of horticultural fleece and then try to carry it away. I can imagine him scuttling home, so proud of himself, with a duvet  to cover the babies. The Missus tolerates mice in the garden, she has a grudging love of them. But rabbits, on the other hand, are so destructive. They have bitten off the second row of peas level with the soil.

The fruit harvest is going to be good. Our apple trees are loaded, except the old Howgate Wonder, which never is, but what it does have weigh nearly a pound an apple. They are green when ripe, sweet and juicy. One apple is enough for two and they store on the branch through the winter. Our cherry plum trees are full of small fruit. Called *Prunus cerasifera* (myrobalan) but in Wiltshire named Mirabel, the pigs love them and scrunch them whole. Cracking the stones seems to give them great pleasure. For us they provide great homemade jam.

SEPTEMBER

The lovely weather goes on and on; I know we have had a little rain a couple of days ago and the nights are a lot colder, but the bees keep buzzing, the butterflies keep flitting, the swallows swipe the sky, the sparrows still squabble and the pigeons keep cooing in the ash tree. Soon we will be blessed with nature's autumn colours, one of the pleasures of this time of the year. Another is picking sloes for sloe gin.

We've had a couple of humming bird hawk moths in the garden. These moths are really spectacular; not that they're big or flash, it's that they hover in front of flowers and stick their long proboscis into them to sip nectar. Their wing-beat is so fast you cannot see them, only their thick bodies. They fly at a terrific speed and, like the painted lady and clouded yellow, they too fly over from France.

It has been a great delight to have the return of the hedgehogs at Long Ash after many years of absence. They feed on snails, slugs, rats and mice and, according to my little *Observer* book, vipers as well, to whose poison they are immune. They do have one predator, the badger. This is probably why they have been so scarce as we have had many badgers on the farm. It is very comforting to know that the friendly hedgehog snores as well as the rest of us.

~

I go gliding most Saturdays and from aloft it's a good way to see the changing colours of the countryside during the year. There is a general brownness now, with most arable fields ploughed or cultivated. The trees and hedges have a tinge of brown upon their leaves that contrasts with the autumn flush of green grass. The black squares like funeral shrouds have gone; they were the ripe bean fields, now harvested, that lie spent and grey, as I wheel above in silence.

We went out riding the other morning. The Missus has a new horse, a rather smart, not to say, classy piebald* with a wall eye*. She's 15½ hands. I ride Tilly (the Tank), an overweight skewbald* cob*. She's like a short-wheelbase Land Rover with no power steering and no brakes. But she is lovely, sweet-natured and placid. She's a pony. Anything up to 14½ hands is classed as such and everything over is officially a horse. So we were out riding, nearly down to the end of Limekiln Lane as it meets Aller Lane, when I spotted a purple hairstreak butterfly. They look black, but as they flutter the sun catches the incredible purple. This unusual butterfly is a real feather in one's cap. It has been nice to see the cinnabar moth. Their yellow-and-black-striped caterpillars live on ragwort. Also the unusual red underwing moth, as opposed to the yellow one, which is often found hidden away in daytime.

We came across (wild) hops growing on the north side of the Hilton playing field. We wondered if 50 years ago the Crown Inn, which used to be at the far end of Duck Street, ever brewed their own beer. I can remember when the Churchill family kept the pub and they didn't then. The hops for the brewery at Milton Abbas, which closed in 1952, were originally grown at Milborne St Andrew a long time ago. This brewery would have supplied beer to the Hilton pub.

～

The swallows have gone, on the same date as last year. The Missus hates their return to Africa as it signifies for her the end of summer. But this month we have had blissfully quiet weather – the 'stillness of September', a slow, calm, mellow mood as nature prepares for slumber and winter. The trees look tired and their leaves hang limply in the airless afternoons. The blue skies carry big fair-weather clouds, and below, a cloud of dust follows the tractor that works a tilth* to sow winter barley.

On misty mornings, cobwebs are strung up in the squares of the pig fences and hitched on the tall woody weeds and brittle cocksfoot grasses. The old men say thunder rain carries nitrogen, that's why the grass grows so well after it falls. Other parts have had heavy thunder showers, but in this bit of the parish we've had virtually none at all. I see from my diaries we have had only around a third of the amount of rain we normally have, up to this time of year. Devil's Brook has dried up at Dewlish Mill. This has never been known before in living memory and it is only 2 miles from its source at Pleck, Higher Ansty. Most of its way it is only a trickle and choked with weeds and watercress.

The lack of rain has made it a wonderful year for blackberries – the Six Acre hedge along the Badger Bank is loaded with them – but not for hazelnuts which have dropped off and are empty when opened. Our cobnuts are the same, with fallen nuts and leaves turned brown.

The common ivy is festooned with its balls of tiny spiky flowers. They are covered with hoverflies and a few bees; too few bees these days. It's always baffled me why ivy flowers in autumn and fruits in the spring (the opposite of other plants). Pigeons love to gorge on the small black berries.

~

It is a bounteous year for hedge fruits – nuts, sloes, haws, hips and elderberries. The long dry period must have made the trees and shrubs believe they might be in danger of dying out. We have two young pigs that have learnt to pick blackberries, even sitting up on their hams to reach the higher ones.

The Dorset County Show was a good show, with many more stall exhibitors this year. In the 1950s it thrived too, when there were many feed and corn merchants, sadly now all gone – firms like Blandford & Webb, Dorset Farmers, Christopher Hills and the like, whose marquees were a familiar sight. It was the custom to have lunch and tea and a drink with them. The food and drink were copious. Father would meet up with his farming friends and they'd go from tent to tent swilling down free whiskys and become more animated and unsteady throughout the day. One year, I remember, Christopher Hills put on badger's ham* sandwiches. Imagine the outcry if it happened today? Everybody had a good day. People dressed up, the men in country tweeds and the women in colourful dresses, some wore hats as well. At the end of the day, the now redder-faced farmers could be seen threading their erratic ways like sheep through the parked cars, followed by their wives, weighed down with children and brown carrier bags.

We see so few field mushrooms today. Mother used to get us up at 5.30 a.m. to pick mushrooms. She'd take them, still with dew on because they weighed more, to Bournemouth to sell. We used to be sent out, with old steel dinner knives which you cleaned with a burnt cork, to collect mushrooms over Mr Voss's land, from Gallows Corner over Louthlees and Beeches and Big Common to Parsonage Farm and back via Little Common. We would get bored and throw our knives in the air to get them to stick in the ground. We lost so many that they must still be ploughing them up today.

The other afternoon when I climbed up into the feed trailer to fill the box on the quad-bike with pig nuts, there was a weasel in a corner. In the old days I would have smacked him with the shovel for all the chicks he had taken from birds' nests and the chicks he'd killed when the Missus had put them out with the broody hen. I put my hand on the shovel and he sat up in defence. 'I suppose you are here to kill the mice?', I said. I swear he nodded twice before he darted away.

OCTOBER

The swallows have gone and so have the last of our runner beans. One tends to get fed up with them when you have been picking them since the middle of June.

In the woods there are crunchy leaves to scuff, the smell of autumn and a wonderful crop of chestnuts. We must have picked a bucketful and all for free. The prickly outer covering is easily dealt with by stamping on them and the nuts burst out under the pressure. Raw or roasted they're lovely now the nights are drawing in.

We had one of those gorgeous golden days recently, when the grass is covered with spiders' threads. It's when you see 'gossamer', a passing floating thread with a tiny spider suspended like a parachutist. This wondrous spider activity is a sign of rain; we had some later, though only a drop fell.

We never see glow worms now. By chance, I read an article that described why. It's because of light pollution; those people who leave their outside lights on in towns and cities, and the illuminated motorways and junctions. The glow worm needs darkness, real darkness, to thrive and to mate. Generating power for a 100-Watt bulb, left on at night all year, releases approximately ¼ ton of carbon dioxide into the atmosphere, encouraging global warming (information taken from the magazine of the CPRE). In town the sky is so lit up you cannot see the stars. Light from them takes hundreds of thousands, even millions of years to reach our eyes; what a pity to lose it in the last split seconds of its journey.

Last week while walking the dogs alongside a blackthorn hedge laden with sloes, we saw a fox eating something. We were downwind of him. Henley, my black Labrador, got within 5 yards. The fox was eating sloes, which must have tasted horrible, but I guess he was desperate.

~

Some say that a good crop of hawthorn berries points to a harsh winter. Probably not; it more likely shows how good the spring and summer were for the setting of the berries. But there has been a tremendous flush of growth recently. The old men say, 'Nature always provides', so maybe a hard winter is on the cards.

We have a hedgehog in our hedgehog box in the garden. The box has a short entrance tunnel and is filled with hay and dry leaves.

We see them trundling along the path after dark.

Up in the woods there are many squirrels on the ground that the dogs chase after. In the summer they are up in the trees, but come October they're all down picking up hazels. The pigeons feed on the beechmast* and we gather up the ripe chestnuts. The squirrel does not make a round hole in the side of the hazelnut, but mice do. If you're lucky enough to find a perfectly round hole with smooth edges, it's the work of the dormouse. The squirrel splits them open, leaving two equal halves.

When we were boys we could crack hazels open with our teeth; now they are a bit 'dagetty'*, to use an old Dorset word, we use our pocket knives. Scrape away at the pointed end until a dark line appears across it. You have reached the inside. Put the point of your blade into the crack and twist. Your nut will split cleanly into two.

Now with falling leaves and spent undergrowth in the hedgerows, there are plenty of berries for all. Perhaps this is why the bird life is quiet in the garden; they have all gone to the hedges and woods.

Blue tit

The blue tits are particularly absent and all the swallows have gone too. Autumn fruits of chestnut, beechmast, hazelnut and acorn are ripe and falling on a carpet of leaves. The horse chestnut ('conker tree') is not a native of Britain. It was introduced during the 17th century and has no relative in this country. The sweet or Spanish chestnut has been here a lot longer; the Romans brought it with them. It is one of the large family of catkin-bearing trees.

Jackdaw

I heard a blackbird giving his 'pink, pink, pink' alarm call up at the old Top Barn from the garden at dusk one evening. No doubt a fox was slinking by beneath his perch. Another quiet afternoon I heard a commotion some way off and saw two crows mobbing a raven; it croaked its annoyance while diving from its attackers. What struck me was the difference in size of them, the raven being almost twice that of the crows. The jackdaw, another member of the Corvid family, is smaller than the crow and often makes its nest in chimney pots. It is easily recognised by its grey head and neck.

After we had seen two little hedgehogs the Missus started feeding them. They must weigh half a pound at winter's start to be alive next spring. As they were so small, she put hedgehog food out for them. One crawled into her hand. Now seven come! What is it about hogs, hedge or domestic? They tug our heartstrings.

When driving to town the other day, on Warren Hill between Dewlish and Puddletown, a sparrowhawk flew straight at us and under the Land Rover. I looked in the rear-view mirror and it was standing in the road with its head up, strutting about. This amply illustrates the amazing flying skill of this much maligned hawk. It is true they chase and take small songbirds, blue tits mainly, but there is no shortage of these and the beautiful little hawk is programmed to eat small birds after all.

—

Darkness and damp lay heavy in our fog-bound valley at the bottom of Long Ash hill. All was still except for the continual dripping of the trees. Sounds carried clear and far. A mile away, I heard Hilton Church strike three and over the hill the Abbey schoolboys cheering on their first XV team. Two or three days later, the wind backed to the south-west and blew hard to make all the leaves turn up and show their undersides – a sure sign of rain, as the old men always say. Suddenly, it became very mild as the warm front came through.

The wind slipped under the cloud and brought the longed-for rain. The next day the grass had grown 2 inches because the soil was still so warm and the weather so mild.

There is an abundance of toadflax on the banks and verges at the roadsides. I've never seen such a multitude on the Bere Regis by-pass. Toadflax looks like flax before it flowers, hence its Latin name *Linaria*. In Dorset it is called 'butter and eggs', because its flowers are orange and yellow. Toadflax is a devil in the garden, spreading like wildfire by its roots, but for all that it is very pretty. The little flower head is like a 'snap dragon'. When we were children we would squeeze the sides to make the 'mouth open'. By manipulating it we could get the flowers to 'talk', as with a ventriloquist and his dummy – 'Gockle o' geer, gockle o' geer!'

Last Tuesday I was stood by the yard gate, facing the road and the farm buildings, unlocking the padlock and chain. As I fiddled with the key a rabbit ran from behind me and almost jumped over my foot. A second later a stoat followed it, just missing me. I watched in amazement as they crossed the road, the stoat chasing the rabbit. They turned and ran towards the farmhouse backdoor and out of sight. Three seconds later they came back one behind the other, re-crossed the road, passed over my boot, through the yard and fence, up the bank, and were gone! Stoats will throw themselves about by contorting their bodies to mesmerise their prey, aided it is said by a parasitic worm that enters the stoat's brain by its nose and eventually kills it. As stoats appear not to have any predators, except man, I can believe it. Sheep have a condition called 'gid' which is caused by a worm that goes up one of their nostrils and into one side of the brain. The poor sheep runs around in unsteady circles and often falls over. In times past it was said the old shepherds would punch the affected sheep in the head – they must have had fists of iron, a sheep's head is very hard – to crack the scull, to loosen the worm and cure the sheep.

NOVEMBER

The rain has arrived after a very mild and unseasonable spell, and so have the various forms of fungi. Sadly we found very few mushrooms, just enough for the pan for a couple of breakfasts. I

Song thrush

reckon we will have another mild, wet winter. A mob of fieldfares came and ate all our crab apples in a day and then flew on to their next feast. Related to our song thrush, they come from Scandinavia and usually foretell cold weather as they migrate south as it gets colder, ending up in Europe. They love holly berries. Now is the time to pick it if you want berried holly for Christmas, it will keep well in a bucket of water.

I have made six tit boxes, three songbird boxes and three bat boxes. After they took off all the roofs from the old thatched barn, farmhouse and buildings to replace the timbers, all the bats disappeared. I positioned these nest boxes very carefully, fixing them so they face north or northeast. They must face out of the full sun and away from the rain. It is important to get them up before winter so that the birds get used to them ready for spring. I have already seen a couple of tits using one of them.

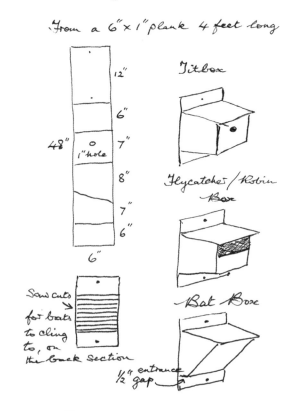

From a 6" x 1" plank 4 feet long

48"

12"
6"
7"   o 1"hole
8"
7"
6"

6"

Titbox

Flycatcher / Robin Box

Saw cuts for bats to cling to, on the back section

Bat Box

1/2" entrance gap

The leaves are all down now and, with the wet, have gone from crunchy to mushy, with that lovely damp, mossy scent. While walking the dogs at Gallows Corner, we heard a stone curlew cry from Long Close. It is about 4 years since we heard one. I don't think I have ever seen one here, only heard its distinctive call. I remember many years ago when we were camping at Ravensglass by the side of the

Stone curlew

Esk estuary, the melodious and bubbly call of hundreds of curlews as they waded in the shallows and we listened from our sleeping bags. I have never forgotten that wonderful early morning sound.

The roe deer are reappearing in increasing numbers now that summer's gone. They tend to creep away to the woods and spinneys* in summer. The tall maize gives them an excellent refuge and you can rarely see them when the corn is in ear. Sometimes a dark Y-shape is glimpsed against the green of the crop as they put their heads up to home in on your scent or sound.

Deer have poor eyesight, or, perhaps more precisely, they have unintelligent sight. If you keep your outline against a tree or hedge, you can creep up to within 20 yards, downwind of one. You must stop every time he puts his head up. Move only when he has his head down to graze or when he turns away from you. They are magnificent animals with their demure eyes and mealy-coloured* mouths. They bound away with their white tail-ends and with such effortless speed and grace.

The male red and fallow deer are always called 'stags', whereas the male roe deer is a 'buck'. The young deer is named a 'pricket'*. Roe deer live in small family groups, the doe (the female) with both this and last year's fawns; often she will have twins. Their territory is really quite small, maybe only two large fields. It is surprising therefore that they cannot be kept in captivity. Being fenced in causes them great distress. Red deer are farmed and fallow are kept for ornamentation in parkland, but not the roe, they are far too beautiful to be 'caged'. The roe has an aristocratic air which is surely deserved. They were obviously created on one of God's good days.

It seems to have been a good autumn for fungi. I have noticed some toadstools that have been nibbled. Rabbits do this and the big chunks missing are the work of the deer. You will never find deer amongst sheep and rarely will you see them in the same field as cattle.

~

Our great big cat has caught two weasels. To my knowledge he's only ever caught six mice in his life and never a bird. To catch and kill a weasel must have been some job, they're very ferocious; and I always thought of him as a girt, dozey dollop.

In the woods the trees have colour and still lots of leaf. Earlier we had ridden out on the horses in bright sunshine and had felt the warmth and pleasure to be out on such a day. At Kingsgate, we saw a late red admiral on a bramble patch. We turned up the drove towards Retreat and saw another on the wing. Retreat never was a monk's retreat, as some think; Baron Hambro from Denmark, who bought the Milton Estate in 1852, built it as a keeper's cottage. And it never used to be called Retreat, it was Beech Clump because of the clump of big trees that stood before it.

I suppose it has been the wettest November in anyone's memory. I measured well over 10 inches. We have had other months that have been incredibly wet according to my diaries but none more than this. I notice in January after the drought year of 1976 we had just over 9 inches. This doesn't come anywhere near the all-time UK record for rain on one day. On the 18th of July 1955, 11 inches fell at Martinstown here in Dorset over 10 hours. This remarkable amount was measured by a Mr N.I. Symons of the village, in a month that was one of the driest that year. It must be said though that November is normally our wettest month.

~

The old men used to say October was the month of colour. But now the vivid picture extends well into November. The glorious sight of burnished beeches warms our hearts even in December.

It seems odd to me that the ash is the last tree to be clothed in leaves and the first to lose them in the autumn. The ash does not have dense foliage like the beech and so it looks airy and light. There is an old superstition regarding this useful tree; it was thought that if a diseased or crippled child was passed through a cleft in an ash tree trunk the child would be cured. The spokes of wagon wheels were nearly always made of ash and its wood is still used for tool handles.

Martinmas (the 11th of November) was as it should be, a lovely sunny day, and there followed a short spell of mild weather. St Martin is the patron saint of tramps, farmers and reformed drunks. The day was preceded by a few crystal sunny days, when the sky was raked free of clouds and it was really warm. Gnats formed their ever-moving column, forever dancing up and down by the wicket gate in a sun trap. Later, in a windless night, hung a moon low in the sky. A dog fox's bark mingled with the moonlight and the sound of a hooting owl, as it searched the dew-drenched meadows for a mate. So, as the door of the old year begins to close, nature is already starting over again.

DECEMBER

One day when it was blowing hard, we were on horseback at the top of Long Ash hill and the rooks were playing what the old men used to call 'crook-neck'. They fly up and then drop down in the shape of a shepherd's crook. It is a sign of bad weather to come.

SIGNS OF RAIN

The hollow winds begin to blow,
The sky looks black, the glass is low,
The soot falls down, the spaniels sleep,
And spiders from their cobwebs creep.

Last night the sun went pale to bed,
The moon in a halo hid her head.
The brooding shepherd heaves a sigh,
To see a rainbow span the sky.

The walls are damp, the ditches smell,
Closed is the pink-eye pimpernel.
Hark! How the chairs and tables crack,
Old Betty's joints are on the rack.

Loud quack the ducks, the peacocks cry,
The distant hills are looking nigh,
The dog so altered in his taste,
Quits mutton bones on grass to feast.

How restless are the snorting swine,
The busy flies disturb the kine.
Low o'er the grass the swallow wings,
The cricket, too, how sharp she sings.

Puss on the hearth, with velvet paws,
Sits wiping o'er her whiskered jaws.
Thro' the clear streams the fishes rise,
And nimbly catch the incautious flies.

The glow-worm, luminous and bright,
Illumed the dewy dell last night.
At dusk a squalid toad was seen,
Hopping and squalling o'er the green.

The whirling wind the dust obeys,
And in a rapid eddy plays.
The frog has changed his yellow vest,
And in a russet coat is dressed.

Oh! See you rooks how odd their flight,
They imitate the gliding kite
And head long downward seem to fall
As if they felt the piercing ball.

'Twill surely rain, I see with sorrow,
Our jaunt must be put off tomorrow.

(Dr Edward Jenner (1749–1823), a country doctor)

Sparrow

Late last night I went to see a sow that's inside with her piglets and found two sparrows in the straw with the piglets under the heat lamp. Next morning I found that the sow had flattened one of them, poor thing.

The wildlife highlight here at Long Ash was the visit of a pair of goldcrests, which stayed with us for 4 days. The goldcrest is our smallest bird, a quarter of an inch smaller than our wren or 'stumpy' as we call the wren in Dorset. The goldcrest has a distinctive gold stripe on the top of its head. They make a beautiful nest which they suspend like a little shopping basket beneath conifer branches.

Goldcrest

⁓

Time was when we were encouraged to cut the ivy off the trees for fear of it throttling them and the winter wind tearing through a mop-head of ivy to topple a hedgerow tree. It is good practice now to leave the ivy as a nest and roost cover for small birds and not so small. There's a cock pheasant that 'cocks-up'* as he goes to roost every evening in the old ivy-covered thorn at the bottom of the field.

At this time of year, the pigeons feast on ivy berries. As I walk up the thorn hedge overrun with ivy, they crash out in a grey cloud of fast flapping wings. It's amazing how they gorge themselves on the berries. When I used to do a bit of pigeon shooting with the decoy pigeons spread out in an arc, many times their crops* would burst as they hit the ground with a thud, they were so full.

Pheasant

That Wednesday, a week before Christmas, what a morning! The sun came up like a big red ball, the air as pure as well water, ice upon the road and hoar frost over all. There was a heavy rhythmic breathing of the sow and litter in her ark, with a little cloud of steam puffing out of the doorway.

I turned off the 'phut, phut, phut' of the quad-bike. A magpie in silent swoop landed just three posts away from me, the cheek of him! He bided his time until I fed the old sow and moved on, then he stole from her heap of nuts. The old sow grunted and emerged from her warm bed to gobble up her feed and a robin sang his happy refrain from the sycamore behind me. Then the moment was broken as a pigeon clattered out of a holly tree, but the robin kept singing for Christmas.

Magpies

Buzzards

It was more than a fortnight that we had those still grey days – those murky mild days when you could hear for miles and walk outside in your slippers, the ground was so dry.

I took the dogs for a walk to Gallows Corner and the long side of Brooklands towards Bagber Buildings. There was no wind, no sun. A buzzard mewed four fields away. I could hear its call plain as plain. The dogs trotted through the crisp dry leaves, two cock pheasants got up noisily and ran the hedge in front of us. Sky strained at her long leash,

Hen pheasant

happy Henley at my heel. We went through the next gate, the two dogs eyeing the two old cocks as they ran the length of the next hedge. In the corner in a bit of rough grass a hen pheasant crouched, a maiden with such innocent eyes and brown-laced beige feathers. I could imagine how hard her heart thumped within her warm breast. The dogs did not spot her and although my booted foot was so close to her, she just lowered her head until I passed. Bagber Buildings had an eerie look as the mist rolled down the slope towards them.

The copse behind had the mist laced amongst leafless oaks. Pigeons sought sanctuary as they flap, flapped, stalled and glided to their roost. A weasel crossed the track in front of us, and a squirrel scampered bandy legged from where the pheasant feeder stood to the copse and up a craggy oak.

That morning there was snow as I went with the milk can to get the milk. The hawthorns lining Birmingham Lane were crowded with 200 fieldfares. They needed their breakfasts and so did I.

—

The afternoon was bright and windy when we went out with the dogs. The sun, low in the sky, backlit scudding clouds that raced over us with beams of sunlight in between. Like searchlights they swept the silent fields to disappear over the lane and light the twisted little oaks and gaunt ash trees against a leaden sky. A cock pheasant called and was answered by another a long way off.

A buzzard drifted high above and then swooped low over the dark hedge and yellowed grass. It used the wind, soaring upwards to catch the sun on its wings. Puffed-up pigeons sat on bare boughs, watching our approach, then suddenly bursting into the cold air with such a noise they disturbed our mellow mood of peacefulness.

Pigeons

Time was when the Boxing Day Shoot was the farmers' shoot-. Local farmers and village worthies (elders) walked each other's hedges, spinneys and root crops, on the lookout for rabbits, a few pheasants, pigeons and the odd partridge. Each farmer brought one of his labourers or young sons who knew what they were about. They carried favourite sticks to beat the hedges to get the birds to run down them to a flushing point. The 'beaters' would also line out across a field of roots and walk slowly, beating towards the 'guns'.

Partridges

No man with a gun, and a wonderful variety of old fowling pieces* there were, was allowed to shoot a low bird. It was a wonderfully good-humoured day with a great deal of banter and raised voices; not the slow straight line of silent discipline of the big, so-called posh shoots where punctuality, pressure and pheasants in plenty are demanded.

—

The night before New Year's Eve was extraordinarily mild. I was out late with the dogs, just thinking that I didn't want my coat on, when a pair of ducks, returning from a feed in some moonlit, muddy meadow, whistled overhead and disappeared into the warm, soft-scented night. As I stood there staring up into the familiar yellow face of the moon, five tawny owls hooted to one another from five directions. I'll never understand the language of their music, but it sealed beautifully the softness of the night and the end of the year.

About the Author

The author and his wife Maureen, a farmer's daughter, are both Dorset born and bred. They met at a Sturminster Newton Young Farmers Club meeting and 2 years later married, as many of their young farming friends did in the 1960s. They have always had so much in common: the love of trees, wild flowers, wild birds of the countryside, the ever-changing skies, all natural history and country matters. Pigs have always been a big interest and cattle too in their farming way of life, now and before when they were children. Andy's father kept a herd of pedigree Large White sows and Maureen's dad had Saddlebacks, which he crossed with a Large White boar. Both of them are extremely practical people, able to turn their hands to anything. Maureen is an expert gardener, whereas the author taught himself to thatch and consequently thatched all the Listed buildings on the farm twice over, and did a few private jobs as well. The author has never worked for anyone else, only his father for a while, and always at Long Ash Farm.

Looking Back

The following photographs give a flavour of country life from the past. Although farm work was labour intensive in those days, there was a great sense of achievement and the satisfaction of working together.

Picnic in the hayfield 1949. *Clockwise from bottom left:* Nigel (my twin brother), Granny Case (Ruth), Auntie Lizzy Lawford (Ruth's sister), Roger (my elder brother), Mother (Molly), Dad (Gerry), Ann (our landgirl) and me. Picnics have always been a great delight for me.

Loading up some very heavy hay bales in 1959 from Silverstone Field with the trailed elevator. In the background is the landmark Girt Down Clump above our farm.

Rick building 1950. *Stood from left to right:* Auntie Florie Andrews, Uncle Clem Andrews, Grandfather Bob Bishop, Cliff Cook, father Gerry Case, Bill Elsworth from Longclose Farm, and Bill Hillier of Milton Abbas on the rick. Uncle Clem was a grain and seed merchant from Poole Quay.

Father driving our 10-ft-cut Massey-Ferguson 788 combine harvester in Gallows Corner Field, 1963.

Me shearing one of our Scotch halfbred ewes (a cross between the Border Leicester and Cheviot) on the wooden elm shearing floor in our thatched barn, 1964.

Father and I dipping our flock to prevent 'fly-strike' in the sheep dip at Long Ash, 1962.

1962 (*from left to right*): me, Salvador, our Spanish live-in worker, Nigel, my twin, and Trudy, our Labrador. Salvador has just backed a trailer full of hay into the 'Top Barn' to unload. He's driving our Massey-Ferguson 35.

One of our Large White fattening pigs, 1958. My father kept a pedigree herd of Large Whites which started my love of pigs.

Glossary

beating – in driven pheasant shoots, a team of people called beaters walk through cover crops (of kale, other crops or woodland) to drive the birds therein to the shooters (guns)

beechmast – the edible seed of the beech tree

broody hen – a hen that, having laid her clutch of eggs, sits or incubates them until the chicks hatch

call duck – a duck used to decoy others into a fabricated tunnel so that they swim into the trap at the end. There is also a breed of duck called a call duck

calyx – the green enclosure that opens to allow a flower to bloom

canvases – the means whereby the cut corn is taken through the binder before it is bound into a sheaf

cart rope – for tying on a trailer-load of hay or straw, traditionally 60 ft long

Charlie – hunting name for a fox

cob (horse) – a heavily built pony or horse, often used for pulling a trap or cart

cocksfoot – a coarse, drought-resistant grass which grows in clumps or tussocks

cocks-up – when a cock pheasant goes to roost he makes an awful racket for a bit and this is known as 'cocking-up'

crop (bird's) – an enlarged part of a bird's throat (gullet) in which food is stored prior to digestion

dagetty – flimsy (Dorset dialect)

dog days – the days when Sirius the Dog Star (the brightest star in the sky) rises and sets with the sun, extending from about 3 July to 11 August

dry sow – a sow not in milk and without piglets at foot

farrowing – a sow giving birth

fodder beet – a sweet root grown for feed for cattle and pigs

fowling piece – an old gun usually of the flintlock mechanism

gilt – a female pig that has not yet had piglets (*elt* in Dorset dialect)

glean – to pick up by hand with a basket the unthreshed heads of corn after a field has been harvested

ham (badger's) – the 'backside' or fleshy top of the back leg

heifer – the name for a cow before or just after she has had her first calf

hiled – the making of a 'hile' or 'stook' (Dorset dialect; see *stooks*)

hoar frost – a white ground frost, also called a grass frost

leather-jacket – the grub of the crane fly or 'daddy long-legs'

mealy-coloured – pale coloured or buff

melanistic – the dark or black form of animals and insects

mouldboard – or to use the old word 'turn furrow', for it does just that

pig nuts – pig meal that is put through a cuber to produce 'nuts' or 'pencils', generally sold by the feed merchant

piebald – black and white

pitch-hole – a position half way up on the side of a rick where a boy pitches sheaves to the rick builder

pricket – a young roe buck (deer) which has just started growing his antlers

rumen – the largest of the four stomachs of a cow

silage – grass preserved by pressing and sealing as winter keep for cows

skewbald – brown and white

spar copse – a small woodland of hazel bushes which are coppiced every 7 years to make spars for thatching

spinney – a little patch of woodland

squibs – young pigeons still fed by their parents ('squeakers' in Dorset dialect)

stooks (shocks) – sheaves of corn standing on their butt ends, usually 8–12 in number, so that the grain dries out before they are put into the rick ('a hile' in Dorset dialect)

sward – the grassy surface of land, turf or pasture

tilth – the finish produced after a field is prepared ready for planting

wall eye – a blue or grey eye with the other eye the normal colour; it is possible to find an animal with two wall eyes

wicket – a gate made of vertical staves (strips of wood)

Index

kingfisher 17–18
Kingcombe 15
Kingsgate 17, 50
kite, red 17

magpie 8, 23, 55
Martinmas 51
Martinstown 50
May blossom 19
May Day 19
Milborne St Andrew 41
Milton Abbas 21, 26, 41, 50
mole 4
Monmoth Down 26
moth 40, 41
mouldboard 5, 18, 65
mugwort 37
mushroom 37, 43, 48

Newton 18, 25
nuthatch 3

owl 9, 12, 51, 57
oxen 6
Oxford Sandy and Black 2, 20, 22,
   58, 59

partridge 26, 57
peewit 1, 3, 4
pheasant 4, 8, 9, 10, 12, 26, 54, 55,
   56, 57, 64
Piddletrenthide 16
pigeon 12, 31–2, 42, 45, 54, 56, 65
pigs
   farrowing 2–3, 29, 64
   sunburn 29
   wallowing 29
ploughing 5–6, 10, 18
plum 35, 39

rabbit 10, 13, 31, 33, 39, 47, 50
raspberry 31
raven 1, 13, 46
Retreat 50
rick building 33–4, 61, 65

robin 10, 14, 55
rolling the ground 8–9, 10
rook 7, 10, 17–18, 28, 52

Sandhills 16
sheaves 33, 65
Sherborne 16
shooting 7, 12, 26, 54, 57, 64
shrew 12
silage 35, 65
skylark 1, 25
sloe 14, 40, 42, 44
song thrush 3, 18, 48
sparrow 1, 15, 40, 56
sparrowhawk 46
spider 42, 44, 46
squirrel 4, 45, 56
St Mark's fly 15
starling 32, 37
stoat 17, 31, 47
stone curlew 49
stooks 33–4, 65
swallow 15, 18, 30, 37, 40, 41, 44,
   45
Sydling 16

Thorncombe 15
tit 1, 48
   blue 45, 46
   long-tailed 1, 3, 11
toadflax 47
treecreeper 13

Varroa disease 12, 24

wagtail, pied 3, 30
Warren Hill 17, 37, 46
weasel 3, 17, 43, 50, 56
weather-lore 7, 14, 22, 25, 42, 44,
   52–3
wood anemone 12, 17, 18
woodpecker 1, 26
Wraxall 16

yew tree 25, 26–7